D1266828

THE
FASTEST
HOUND DOG
IN THE STATE OF MAINE

Books by John Gould

New England Town Meeting
Pre-Natal Care for Fathers
Farmer Takes a Wife
The House That Jacob Built
And One to Grow On
Neither Hay nor Grass
The Fastest Hound Dog in the State of
    Maine

The
Fastest
Hound Dog
in the State of Maine

By JOHN GOULD

Illustrated by F. WENDEROTH SAUNDERS

WILLIAM MORROW AND COMPANY
New York
1953

To the

WHEN archeologists were digging out the ruins of Pompeii, they came upon a beautiful tessellated pavement, and thought it must surely be the exquisite decoration of some rich Roman's holiday villa. It turned out to be merely the patio of his kennel, and the villa itself, when finally found, was far more exquisite even than that. The mosaic work on the patio of the kennel, delicately wrought with Parian marble and jade and onyx and precious gems, spelled out this simple Latin:

CAVE CANEM!

THE WHY,
THE WHEREFORE,
AND THE HOW-COME

LIKE MANY other stories that have appeared from time to time, I didn't really write this one. It would be an untruth to wish that I had, because I don't wish any such a thing. This is true folk material, and its authors must remain forever unknown. Too many people have passed it on down, adding as it came. I have added one word myself (line 224) and am pleased with the improvement.

I don't know, of my own knowledge, if this story has ever been written down before. It has been around a long time, and may have. But it has taken its form orally, and I have here recorded as numerous Maine story-tellers give it. So, to wish I had written it is to wish away its charm, just as we would spoil the old Scottish ballads by learning, suddenly, that they had really been written by Mrs. Eleanor Roosevelt. I think you will agree with me.

The ending of this tale may startle elderly librarians and sensitive folks who have not been

9

extensively exposed to the facts of life, but I make no apology for it. I tell it the way I hear it. I merely point out that dogs will be dogs. I do call the reader's attention to copious and scholarly notes in the back of this book, where a number of academic matters are treated with penetrating analysis, and some scholarship. I suggest the story be taken in one sitting, and the notes saved for later. Do not, as some students do, interrupt the flow of the discourse by turning at odd moments to the appendix.

This story belongs to the times when people sat around, before radio, television and open-air movies. It offers entertainment over a period of time, and thus differs from the quick gag of the modern breed. It is in the tradition of the one-eyed minstrel and wandering troubadour. Ulysses had his Argos, Llewellyn his Gelert, and here is a new background up in Maine.

It is a story that should be told, not read; but if read, it should be read aloud. It should also be pronounced after the Maine fashion. For instance, "fastest" should be pronounced "fahstest" throughout. Dialect is hard to read, and I have not tried to spell Maine speech. Besides, dialect is a matter of sound, and not of orthography, for if you ask a Vermonter how to spell "caow" he will promptly say "c-o-w." So I have skipped the

10

alphabetical gymnastics of so-called dialect, but I doubt if non-Maine accents will add much to the yarn.

Apart from the admitted purpose of monetary gain, the author and artist were moved to production because we feel this story merits a permanent place in American literature, along with others whose places are already secured. I might mention *The Jumping Frog, The Treasurer's Report, The Devil and Daniel Webster*, and perhaps the old yarn of the New York trolley car that got lost. Or, I might mention *The Ballad of Chevy Chase*, to go back before our own time. I think this story deserves study in schools and colleges, where prospective writers could learn a lot from its craftsmanship.

JOHN GOULD

Lisbon Falls, Maine, 1953

NOTE

Wytopitlock and Mattawamkeag are pronounced essentially as written, thus: wit-o-pit-lock and mat-a-warm-keg. Principal stress on the penults.

Both these places exist, but readers are referred to the notes for the explanation of how they happen to figure in this story.

THE
FASTEST
HOUND DOG
IN THE STATE OF MAINE

GOOD MANY times people have asked me how I came to own the fastest hound dog in the State of Maine, and why he was known to be the fastest, and I want to tell it just the way it happened so you'll all know the facts. I came from Wytopitlock, where I was living at the time, down to Mattawamkeag on the Bangor & Aroostook Railroad one day to buy myself a hound dog. Up to Wytopitlock we was hav-

5

10

17

ing a run on long-legged rabbits then, and
I didn't want none of these short-legged dogs
that can run all day and not move any. I
wanted one with rangy pins that could get
close enough to a Wytopitlock rabbit so he'd   15
exert himself and know he was chased. The
short-legged dogs we'd been using was no
good at all, and I says to myself, "The Hell
with that!"

So I set out on purpose to find me a dog   20
that was high-posted, limber and lickety,
clever and able, and why I came down to
Mattawamkeag I don't rightly know, but
I'm quite a cuss on dogs and have a sense of
smelling them out once I know what I want.   25
So here I was in Mattawamkeag and not
knowing a soul there, but I wandered around
thinking if they had a likely dog in those
parts I'd soon find out, and if they warn't,
I'd soon know that, too, and no harm done.   30

Well, I circulated some, and had made up
my mind it was a day thrown away, and I

19

started back to the depot, meaning to pick up a copy of the Bangor Daily *News* to read on the train going home, and to get there quicker I cut across and came up onto the back end of a barn, and when I did I had this premonition of Dog, and I says to myself that I'd been led to this barn by some power unknown.

So I said to myself, "Dog!" And just as I did they commenced to bark, and I'd say offhand without exaggeration that the barn had fifty dogs in it, at least fifty, and just then a little door opened and a fellow stuck his head out and wanted to know what I was up to.

I said I was just cutting across to the Bangor & Aroostook depot, and moved up closer while I was saying it, and when I got close enough to holler above the dogs I said, "What you got in there?"

"In where?" he says.

"In that barn," I says.

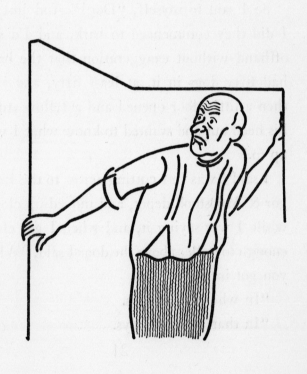

"In what barn?" he says.   55

I could see we warn't getting any place that way, and where I didn't have much time for the train I says, "Sounds like dogs."

"It might be," he says.

I says, "I'm looking for a dog if I find   60
the one I want."

"Mine ain't for sale," he says.

So I says all right, but where I had a few minutes to train time, did he mind if I looked at them, and he said he didn't see no harm   65
in that, so we went in. Well, sir, I never see such a bevy of dogs. He had every kind of dog that the mind of God had ever devised, and some nobody had thought up yet, and on top of that he had crossed them up some-   70
what, but they were all fat and nice and all glad to see me. I patted some of them and made of them, and kept looking for one that might match up with a Wytopitlock rabbit, but I didn't see any that took my fancy, and   75
I got to thinking I'd better be getting on

23

down to the depot.

But something made me dilly-dally, no doubt it was Providence, and all to once over in the far corner I heard a new bark, some dog that hadn't been saying anything was starting in, and for some reason I liked the sound of it. So I says, "What's that?"

"What's what?" he says.

"That barking," I says.

"Dog, I guess," he says.

So I went over, and he had a piece of chicken wire strung kitty-cornered, and where it was back from the window I couldn't rightly see, but I run my hand in, and I got the friendliest lapping I ever had from a dog, and I knew right off that I'd come onto the very dog I was after and no doubt about it. I could tell from the way he lapped that he had a kind heart and a know- ing eye, and his bark was the bark of a hound, and where I held my hand he come up about

Saunders

belt high or so. I made up my mind to have him first and look him over afterward. I was that sure. So I took my hand out and says, "That might be the very dog I want!" 100

"He ain't for sale," the fellow says.

I says, "I take it he's a hound."

"Sort of," he says. "But he ain't for sale."

I says, "Probably ain't much of a dog, 105 then."

"Oh, yes," he says. "He's a good dog, but I'm sentimental over him, and don't plan to let him go."

So looking at my watch I says, "Time's 110 running on and I got a train to catch, so I got to be getting along." I says, "If this dog was for sale, which you say he ain't, and you was to take a liking to me, knowing I could give him a good home," I says, "what price 115 would you put on him?"

"He ain't for sale," he says.

"I know that," I says. "And I'm not interested in him, but if I was to be interested

27

in him, and you was to offer him for sale, 120
what kind of value would you set on him?"

"I don't know," he says. "I ain't thought
of selling him, and ain't put my mind to it."

So I says, "That's true, and I appreciate
your feelings, but what I'm talking is purely 125
supposing-if, and I give you my word I ain't
got the slightest hankering for that dog at
all, and if you was to offer him to me as an
outright present, I doubt if you could make
me take him," I says. "So what I mean is by 130
way of passing the time until the train comes,
and I'd like to have your opinion as to what
a dog like that is worth, so I'd know what
to offer if I ever run up against one like him
that takes my eye." 135

"Well," he says. "Putting it that way I
got to tell you that he's really a valuable
dog."

I says, "That's an opinion, and I respect
your right to hold it, but I was hoping you'd 140
express it in terms of money"—and I slapped

29

my wallet—"so I'd know just how valuable you think he is."

"Well," he says. "He's worth a good deal." 145

I says, "How much is a good deal?"

So he says, "Well, he ain't for sale, as I told you, and I don't want to make no remarks that would mislead you, but if he was for sale, which he ain't, and I was to put a 150 price on him, which I refuse to do, I'd say he was no good to me at all unless he'd fetch —well, let's say about . . . Oh, I'd say about a dollar and a quarter."

"Well," I says. "I admire your honesty 155 and I thank you for your opinion, but I can see that your sentimental attachment to him has given you some erroneous ideas, but if he was for sale, which I understand he ain't, and if I was to be interested in buying him, which 160 I ain't, I don't believe I could possibly bring myself to make an offer for him of anything above seventy-five cents," I says.

31

So the fellow says, "Sold!"

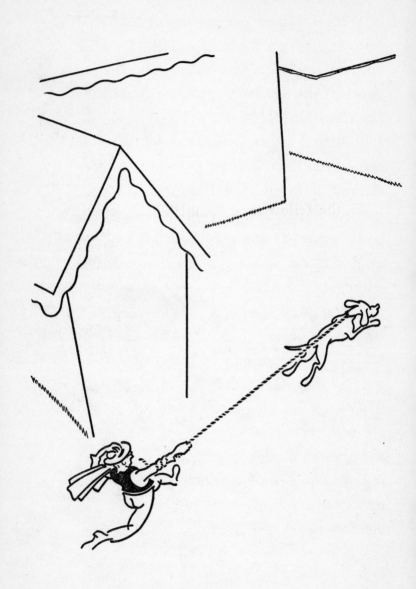

Well, I hauled out my wallet and paid him, and he got me a string, and I tied it onto my new dog and we started out for the depot on the dead run, because I could hear the train putting on the air already. As we run along I watched the dog, and he was 170 certainly as likely-looking as anything I ever clapped an eye to, and I say it as one who has seen dogs, more or less, all my life. He had a beagle's face, and I judged his nose was good, and his back was limber as a willow 175 withe, and the way he picked up his feet and put them down was sweet as a heavenly chorus singing angels' tunes. He had a swing to him, and I chuckled at what we had in store for the rabbits up home at Wytopitlock. 180 They'd got fat loping along in front of our old dogs, and I planned to whittle them down and astonish them a great deal. I was admiring my dog so much I almost forgot to pick up a copy of the Bangor Daily *News*, but I 185 got one, and then I found me a seat and sat

down, and tied the dog to the footrest. He sat up, and I patted him some, and I was proud of him. He had a dewy eye and a buckshot nose, and every fiber of his carcass was laid just the right way. His ears hung good, without too much flop, and every point was a hundred percent with some to spare. I had just said to myself, "I do believe that's the fastest hound dog in the State of Maine, without the shadow of a doubt," when I looked up and the conductor was standing by my seat with the ticket punch in his hand, and he says, "What's that?"

"What's what?" I says.

"That dog," he says. "I presume it is a dog, is it not?"

"It is," I says. "And furthermore," I says, "he's the fastest hound dog in the State of Maine."

"He is?" he says.

I says, "Yes, he is."

"How do you know?" he says.

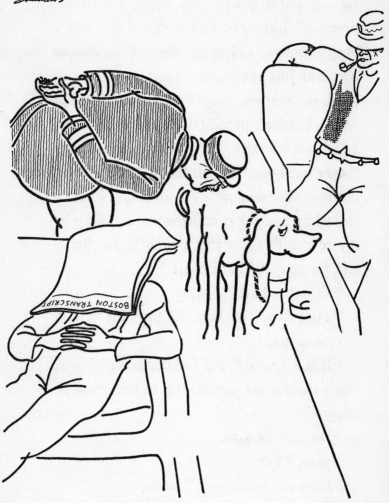

I says, "By the looks of him. Did you ever see a dog like him?" 210

"No," he says. "I never did."

I says, "See how high strung and limber he is. His hind legs is like a kangaroo, and the way his front ones hang on the bias, he couldn't interfere if he had to. That's for 215 speed. Notice his nose and his knowing eye," I says, "and you can see for yourself."

"He don't look so fast to me," he says.

"He is," I says.

"Where'd you get him?" he says. 220

"Right here in Mattawamkeag," I says. "He's bred," I says, patting the dog.

"How's he bred?" he says.

"Down the line," I says. "His late mother was a beagle, as you can see, and for a nose 225 you give me a beagle and I can be happy. Without a doubt she had the longest pedigree papers ever registered, although," I says, "I'm not a hand myself to care about papers if the breeding is good." 230

"That's right," he says. "What was his father?"

"His father," I says, "was mostly Matta-wamkeag, and that's where he gets his ranginess and high-wheeled confirmation."   235

"I see," he says. "Well, you can't take a dog in the coaches on the Bangor & Aroostook Railroad, so you got to get him out of here."

Well, sir, for a minute I was floored, as   240 I hadn't thought of that, but I says, "Well, I got to get this dog home to Wytopitlock and I got a ticket, and I don't see what harm he'll do sitting here at my feet, and where he's the fastest hound dog in the State of   245 Maine it seems as if we might stretch a point."

"The Bangor & Aroostook Railroad," he says, "don't stretch no points, and the rule is no dogs in the coaches, so you got to get   250 him out of here. You can put him in a baggage car, on leash and muzzled," he says.

41

"Well, there," I says. "Now we're talking sense. Which way is the baggage car," I says, "front or back?"   255

"They ain't no baggage car on this train," he says.

"Then," I says, "I got rights, and I plan to take my dog home, so we're going to stay right here."   260

"Oh, no, you ain't," he says. "You got to get him off the train, and you got to get him off quick, because we're only an hour late now, and we don't want to get any later."

So I says, with a sudden bright idea, "I   265
tell you what I'll do then. I'll just tie my dog to the back platform of the last car, and while we run up to Wytopitlock he can trot along behind the train, and it'll give him a little exercise and won't break no rules of the   270
railroad."

So the conductor says, "It might not break any rules of the railroad, but it sure would be a dirty trick on the dog. He'd get drug to

43

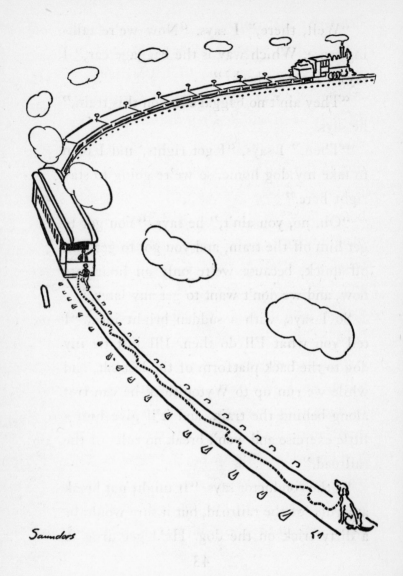

death the first mile."

Well, that kind of hoisted my dander, so I says, "There ain't no train the Bangor & Aroostook runs could drug that dog to death, Mister," I says, and I put real meaning into that mister. I says, "That's the fastest hound dog in the State of Maine, and if you could run your trains half as well, you wouldn't be no hour late right now." That kind of made him set up and take notice, and I could see it was a telling blow. I got up real mad, and untied the string, and the dog and I walked back through the train with our heads held high and not taking any guff from anybody. All the way back the conductor kept telling me I couldn't tie the dog on back, that he'd get drug to death, and it was cruelty to dumb animals.

"This dog ain't so dumb," I says, "but what he could find somebody dumber if he was to look." And I put the dog down on the tracks behind the train and let out the rope to

give him free slack to play around with, and while I was doing it the conductor said something about how he was willing to bet money the dog would never set eyes on Wytopitlock. 300

"Money," I says, "is a born conversationalist"—and I slapped my wallet—"and I'm always keen-eared to hear it talk."

That kind of stopped him for a minute, but he says, "All right, I tell you what I'll 305 do. I'm a sporting man, and I'll just make you a bet. I'll bet you twenty-five cents that dog is dead when we get to Wytopitlock."

"Look," I says, "I'm a sporting man myself, and I don't mind saying so, and I'd just 310 as lief take your money as anybody's, but up to Wytopitlock where I come from it's the same as an insult to mention any such minnow amount as that. If you'll haul out your wallet and make a bet that's got some meat on its 315 ribs, I'm with you and ready to do business." I didn't want him to think I lacked confidence in my dog.

47

So he says, "Well, then you say how much," and he hauled out his wallet. 320

So I says, "Well, it ought to be enough to make it interesting, and I don't think we should mention any sum that wouldn't make it worth while to the dog."

So he says, "How much, then?" 325

So I says, "Well, what do you say to fifty cents?"

"Done!" he says.

So I finished tying on the dog, and we went back in the coach and got a runner to 330 hold the money, and while the conductor went to taking up tickets I sat down and commenced reading the Bangor Daily *News* and put the whole matter out of my mind. I chanced to look up after a while and saw 335 we were humming right along, and I thought to myself that if we kept this up I ought to get home in fair season, and just then the conductor came back and braced himself against my seat and said, "We're going right 340

49

along now."

"Seem to be," I says.

"We've made up forty-five minutes," he said.

"That's good," I says.   345

He says, "How about the dog?"

"What dog is that?" I says.

"The one we tied on back," he says. "He's probably dead by now."

But I had confidence in that dog, so I   350
says, "No, I don't think so, but there's a good way to find out." So we went out back, and there was the dog all right. He warn't even breathing hard, just loping along at an easy gait, holding his head high and lifting   355
the slack of the rope with his teeth, so he wouldn't trip over it, and spacing his steps so the ties came right, and I could see that the conductor was really disappointed. So I says, to rub it in a little, I says, "Do you want   360
to pay me now?"

"No, sir!" he says. "I admit I expected

51

him to be in worse case, but we're still a long ways from Wytopitlock, and your money ain't riding on no sure thing. We still got 365 that long down-grade by Mars Hill, and when we hit that you'll see."

Well, I tried to read the Bangor Daily *News*, but every time I'd get settled down the conductor would come by and want to 370 look at the dog, so we'd go back, and every time we did he was coming along at an easy clip, just gearing his speed to the lay of the ties and not trying to gain any, and I can tell you that conductor was a mighty sick man, 375 thinking how his fifty cents was as good as gone and nothing to show for it.

But he kept saying, "You just wait when we get to that long down-grade by Mars Hill, and he'll be drug to death." 380

Well, I was sitting with one foot up, reading the Bangor Daily *News*, and I turned a page and happened to look out the window, and I almost swallowed my teeth, if I'd had

Saunders

them in, at the way the State of Maine was 385
galloping by. We were hypering. Just tear-
ing, and I says to myself, "That conductor
has got the engineer in cahoots, and they're
piling on the steam just to get my fifty
cents!" And just then the conductor came 390
by, and he had a smile on his face, and I
could see he was pretty pleased at the way
we were going.

He says, "This is that long down-grade
by Mars Hill."   395

I says, "It is?"

"Yes, sir," he says. "And we're moving
right along."

"Does seem so," I says.

"Running thirty-five minutes ahead of 400
schedule," he says.

"Is that so?" I says.

"We generally open things up along in
here," he says.

"Well, I can see we're going right along," 405
I says.

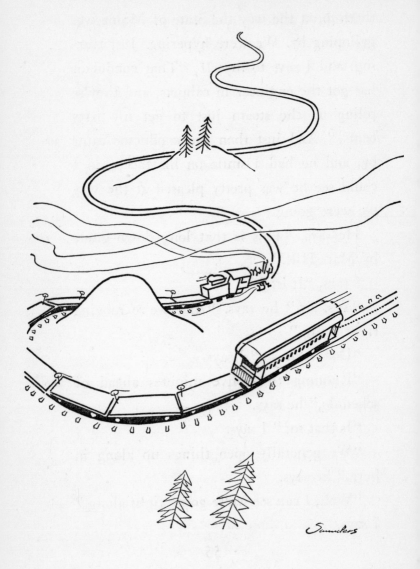

Saunders

He says, "How do you suppose he's making out?"

"Who's that?" I says.

"The dog," he says.

"Oh," I says. "The dog!" I says. "I put him completely out of my mind, I'm glad you spoke of him," I says.

He says, "Don't you think we better go back and look at him?"

"No," I says, "he's all right. You don't need to worry none about him. I don't think the Bangor & Aroostook is likely to bother him much," I says.

"Let's go look at him," he says.

"Well, we can if you want to," I says. "But I doubt if it's going to make you feel any better." To tell you the truth, though, I had begun to mistrust things some, and I didn't like the way the train was high-tailing it along. I do believe that's the fastest speed the Bangor & Aroostook Railroad ever managed to get up to, and I couldn't help think-

ing how much it was costing them in coal
just to protect that fifty cents, and I got to   430
feeling sorry for the fireman, put to all that
trouble just to embarrass me about my new
dog. But I warn't going to let that conductor
see I was fretting, so I makes believe I was
finishing a sentence in the paper, and I lays   435
it down and yawns, and gets up. But when
we got out on the back platform you could
have heard my heart go plunk down into my
stomach, because they warn't no dog there!

"Pay me!" shouts the conductor, and he   440
laughs and carries on just as if fifty cents
was the biggest thing in the world and he
couldn't wait to get home with it.

"Now wait a minute!" I says, sparring
for time. I says, "You got too small an   445
opinion of my dog. I told you this dog was
fast, and you was too smart-aleck to listen
to me. Now the truth is that this dog has just
got tired poking along behind, and I think
he's too fast for the Bangor & Aroostook. In   450

59

my opinion," I says, "he's just trotted up alongside the train to rest a little out of the dust, and I think if we look up along the side of the train we'll find him."

"You might just as well pay," he says. "That dog got drug to death miles back, and you might as well pay."

But I went over to the side of the platform, and the conductor with me, and we were going so fast I almost got my head snapped off when I stuck it out. But by holding our hands against the dust, we could see, and they warn't no dog there, neither, and I was feeling pretty bad about it.

"Pay me!" shouts the conductor, rubbing his hands.

"No, sir!" I says. "You forget, Mister, that they's two sides to every train, and I got confidence in my dog, and I just took the wrong side of the train first. I'll admit you and the engineer cahooted up on me, but that dog has got speed too, and the Bangor &

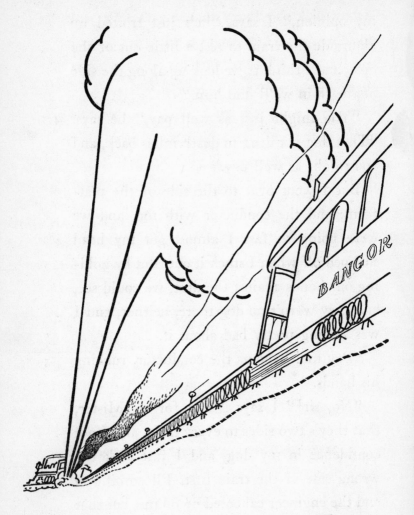

Saunders

Aroostook don't know that dog as well as I do. Now, we'll just look up the other side of the train, and I think you'll find the dog is there all right." 475

So we went over and held our hands against the wind, and looked, and if you ever see a sick conductor, that fellow was your man, because there was my dog, the fastest 480 hound dog in the State of Maine, up alongside the train, running along easy-like on three legs, and wetting down a hot box.

NOTES

ONE should remember that the great bulk of annotated material on some such story as *Hamlet* did not appear all at once. It accumulated thought by thought. I have not exhausted the literary aspects of *The Fastest Hound Dog In The State of Maine* in the remarks which follow, and I hope scholars will add from time to time. I have merely tried to append sufficient explanatory material so those hearing this epic for the first time may appreciate its finer qualities.

J. G.

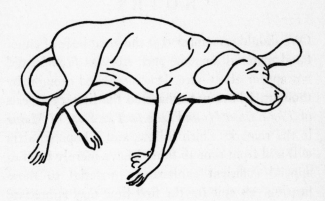

Line 5, . . . *so you'll all know the facts.* All truly Maine stories begin with a strong respect for veracity. This is a well-established technique and needs handling early in the story. Ed Grant used to start his *Story Of My Pet Trout* by recalling that, "It was in the spring of '88, or was it '87? No, it was '88, because in '87 we had a fire at Number Four, and I know it warn't that year." The exact year, naturally, has no importance, but this beginning serves to convey that the narrator is striving to keep everything on a high plane of historical truth.

Line 6, *Wytopitlock . . . to Mattawamkeag.* The geography of this story will bother purists, and to people who look things up on maps we might as well confess that the story is wrong regarding these communities. It isn't far from Wytopitlock to Mattawamkeag, as the hounds run, or vice versa, and other geography in the story (see line 366) indicates that the original minstrel chose these names more for their sound than for their location. He might have selected places better able to stand up when compared to a time table, even if less euphonious. He might, for instance, have come from Presque Isle down to Houlton, in which event Mars Hill would lie between, but he didn't. This sort of thing has been done by many successful authors. Confer the sonnet by John Keats about opening Chapman's Homer, a poem in which Stout Cortez discovers the Pacific Ocean. Mr. Keats was big enough so it didn't matter that his history was off. So, too, does Shakespeare have somebody shoot off a cannon before firearms were invented, but Shakespeare was also a great man and cared not. The thing is explained nicely by Humpty Dumpty, who tells Alice that

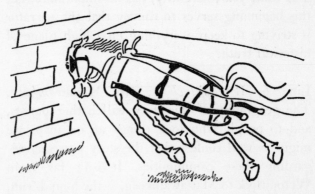

he makes words mean whatever he wants them to mean. People who write in that fashion become immortal, while those who worry about facts continue on academic studies about water power potentials, personal items in the weekly press, or big news magazines. It's like Hod Hunter's horse, who bumped into the stone wall until people thought he was blind. The horse wasn't blind, he just didn't give a damn, so let us not trot to the atlas to check unessential details. Our author might have come from Mooselookmeguntic down to Cobbosseecontee on the Sandy River & Rangeley Lakes R. R., but he didn't.

Line 8, *Bangor & Aroostook Railroad*. The rugged railroaders who operate this northerly line have probably never regarded this story as highly complimentary. But it is too late to complain. The

Bangor & Aroostook is a modern line that efficiently serves Northern Maine with fast freight and passenger facilities.

Line 9, *to buy myself a hound dog*. The double double in this line is interesting. He might, you see, be buying a hound for somebody else, but he isn't. The pronoun is common in Maine talk—bought *himself* a hat, took *himself* to town, got *himself* a ticket. Also, the word *hound* is seldom used without the word *dog*—it might be a hound *puppie*, for instance, or a shepherd *dog*. Maine men economize on words by stating the thing completely the first time. Since he leaves nothing out, he doesn't have to repeat anything. See line 186.

70

Line 11, *long-legged rabbits*. The Maine rabbit is the "snowshoe" kind, and conies are not recognized game animals, although they are found in some parts of the state. A snowshoe rabbit makes a track on the snow that looks as if a six-foot man had gone by carrying a grindstone and two 40-quart cream cans of applejack. It would therefore be understood by his listeners that the story-teller refers to unusually large rabbits, and a kind that demands the attention of an unusual dog. The emphasis on size is gained simply by the adjective "long-legged." Ordinary Maine rabbits are longer legged than rabbits anywhere else, except Nova Scotia, where a rabbit has developed which can successfully run up the flats ahead of a Fundy tide.

Line 18, *the Hell with that*. Personally, I deplore the insertion of even this mild word in a story which is otherwise spotlessly clean, but it is good Maine stuff and must be reported accurately. Violence of language need not be a detriment to good narrative, but if you are reading this to children you may want to tone this down to something like, "Oh, fudge on that." Or, you can render *Hell* as *heck*. I once read a French novel in which peasants crossed themselves upon hearing a certain oath, said to be "the vilest curse in the French language." I later found a translator had rendered it as, "Oh, dearie me!" It is sometimes hard to know just what to do, but personally I am in favor of leaving the *Hell* just as we found it.

Line 30, *and no harm done*. The philosophy of this sentence is intense, and is seldom achieved so casually by even the best writers. Stephen Leacock approached it in his delightful line, "Some men play golf, and some do not." It seems to sum up the whole theory of freedom of mind and willingness to take things as they come.

Line 34, The Bangor Daily *News*. An authentic touch. This newspaper purports to be the largest in Maine, and has a unique editorial belief that local columns should be conducted by such purely provincial correspondents as Walter Winchell, Leonard Lyons, Westbrook Pegler, and such as that. Journalists in southern and western parts of Maine theorize that subscribers never read it, because if they did they'd stop subscribing, but this is professional jealousy only. The paper, like the Bangor & Aroostook Railroad, serves its own area well, and a train passenger up that way picks up his copy with the same devotional energy that a Free Will Baptist deacon would expose as he took his Bible to Sabbath services.

Line 45, *a little door opened*. This is sheer use of one of the oldest dramatic devices. The road in the painting leads your eye beyond the hills, and the opening door brings intensity to the narrative. This same device will be found as far back as Plautus, and the man who pokes his head out is confederate to suspense. It is important to notice that this fellow is not described—short or tall, fat or thin, naked or clothed—nor is it necessary. The reader, or listener, does that work automatically, and the story gains speed and vigor. Too many professional writers would stop at this point to say how the man looked, the color of his eyes, did he stoop, or limp. Not here—it is quite enough to have the door open, the fellow appear, and the question follow.

Line 49, *depot*. The word is used throughout Maine for a railway station. It is pronounced *dee-po*.

Line 51, *"What you got in there?"* The reader will be glad to know that this is the precise point in the narrative where one man has decided to buy and the other has decided to sell.

Line 67, *bevy*. I believe this word was added to the story by Mr. Stephen E. Merrill of Brunswick, Maine, whose wife was born in Fort Fairfield, Aroostook County. It is not a true folk touch, but is a substantial, and satisfactory, addition. Its charm lies in the fact that while it was never in the early variants, it *might* have been, and it sounds right. I prefer it to the more common, "pack of dogs."

Line 70, *somewhat*. Somewhat is not a word that precise people would use for the hybridization of dogs, but it does convey a certain wide-open possibility that needs to be captured at this point. It does, however, have the authenticity of frequent use. When Oliver Tuttle fell into the hay baler and came out the other end he was described in the Fort Fairfield *Review* as "somewhat used up." This technique of suggesting infinity by frugal choice of words is common in Maine, and President James S. Bixler of Colby College exemplifies it by telling of the gentleman 86 years old who saw his great-grandmother exhumed to permit a highway to pass. When asked how the old lady looked, he said, "Not too rugged."

Line 86, *I guess*. To guess, in Maine, is equal to documented proof in other places. Sometimes Maine people are quoted in literature as saying, "I reckon," but none ever has yet. To reckon, in Maine, is to add up a column of figures, whereas "calculate" means to opine. Certainly this guess that the barking comes from a dog is, under the circumstances, as astute a piece of reasoning as has been reported in some time. The fact that it turns out to be a dog attests the reasoning powers of the man, and proves him to be reliable.

Line 88, *kitty-cornered*. Quarter-cornered, or cater-cornered, is not understood in Maine, and people generally believe kitty-cornering derives from the game of Puss in the Corner. "Kittring" is middle-west for kitty-cornered.

Line 108, *sentimental*. Unlikely as it may seem, it is still possible to be sentimental over a dog when you have fifty of them. In this instance, however, the word is employed to suggest a good, if nebulous, reason for not wanting to sell.

Line 115, *a good home*. This, again, is a vagueness like the term *sentimental*, supra. It does, however, cancel out the sentimentality as far as the give and take of dickering is concerned, since the owner now knows that his beloved dog will go to a kind, Christian home that doesn't keep late hours. The reader will notice that in the jockeying which follows every objection by one party is neatly met by a counter-objection or waiver by the other party. Upon striking a financial balance, the deal is, of course, concluded.

Line 136, *I got to tell you*. Something which would, of course, never be mentioned if there existed the slightest thought of concluding a sale.

Line 142, *wallet*. I don't know if this word is used elsewhere as it is in Maine. It signifies a leather billfold that will contain about a peck of odds and ends from grocery lists to the deed on the home farm, and money if any is available. It should not be confused with a change pouch, or any style of purse. To slap one ordinarily means to talk in terms of folding money, but some men can slap an empty wallet so it makes quite a racket. In the old days a man often carried both a wallet and a change pouch, the latter with a snap top. Sam Foster used to have one made from an eelskin

about three feet long, and it took Sam so long to skin out a quarter that he seldom spent anything.

Line 157, *sentimental attachment . . . erroneous ideas.* These larger words are not at all out of place in this general discourse. It happens to be a weird habit of Maine men to use big words at surprising times. Every town is bound to have a well-read citizen who sheds high-grade verbiage until everybody knows it. I have always admired a sign I saw on a back-country tinkerer's shop which said, "Automotive Electrician." It is an old Maine expression to "rig a scheme" when something needs doing, and one of my neighbors has adapted that to "fabricate a contrivance."

Line 172, *clapped an eye to*. The other Maine phrase to describe a method of perception runs, "The best thing I ever stuck a tooth in."

Line 177, *heavenly chorus*. This particular description is rendered many ways in the variations of narrative. I have also heard it, ". . . sweet as an angelic host making sweet concord and harmony." Readers should remember that pioneer Maine men took two things seriously—liquor and church. The hymnals and three-hour sermons gave the state familiarity with certain pious expressions

which have remained. It is not uncommon to hear sacred language at profane moments. Incidentally, what quirk of the Maine mind first gave our Saviour a middle initial? It is H. I have imagined it may come from the "I. H. S." of old, but I am not an etymologist and cannot speak with authority.

Line 183, *astonish*. Astonish is commonly used to express a mild degree of being scared to death. A swarm of bees will go up under somebody's skirt, and she will be described as "astonished." This is probably so, and perhaps does justice to the situation as well as any word could.

Line 190, *buckshot nose*. This means good, clear channels in the nostrils, coming to a point so they suggest a double-barreled shotgun. I don't know why, either.

Line 197, *conductor*. Now we come to a cosmic consideration, for a conductor, in Maine, is fair game. The Bangor & Aroostook Railroad, in late years, has been extremely public-relations conscious, and few railroads now operating have done as much, by company policy, to raise the train crews into the realm of human beings. They have discarded the deep blue uniform and have adopted a smart attire midway between a bus-driver and a member of the Canadian Mounted. They have also hired men who know how to speak English in a cultured and friendly way. However, this good intention has not spread to all connecting lines, and there is some ground for feeling that

conductors have not, as a class, ingratiated themselves broadly to the traveling public. It seems as
if this story captures some of this latent friction,
and we find an element of subtle satire in the
way the conductor is duped. Probably the public-
be-damned attitude of many carriers and utilities
finds personification in the conductor, and a kind
of reserve is directed at him for want of a closer
target. For years a certain railroad (not mentioned by name in this book) wouldn't sell a
ticket to a certain town because the train wasn't
scheduled to stop there. Passengers were required
to wait for a later train which did stop. However,
the earlier train always did stop, to pick up a
conductor, and the animosity thus engendered was
of a lively nature, and bloomed like the rose. I
do not wish, in these notes, to stir up the hatred
of any railway corporations, or even to alienate
the Brotherhoods, but it seems essential to touch
on this matter to underline the feeling that obviously prevails in this story. The conductor is certainly a negative character from his first remark.

Line 211, *"I never did."* This line needs oral
punctuation to make it convey its full meaning.
The conductor implies, as he speaks the line, that
he has also been praying nightly since a small boy
that he never would. One time my father went

fishing and caught a long string of eels, chub, hornpout, pickerel, perch, suckers and bass. He held it up to somebody and said, "Did you ever see a string of trout like that?" The man said, "No, I never did." Realization of what the line means will help the reader inflect it.

Line 218, *"He don't look so fast to me."* This is the line from which the famous "shaggy dog" story obviously derives. Readers will observe that the story of *The Fastest Hound Dog In The State of Maine* is *not* a shaggy dog story, for the reason that it has narrative direction, and successfully arrives. This story goes somewhere, a shaggy dog story does not.

A shaggy dog story, by extension and derivation, is one which occupies the attention, but doesn't deliver any goods. If this story were to end on this line ("He don't look so fast to me.") you could change "fastest" to "shaggiest" throughout and have the original shaggy dog story as it first appeared some years ago. However, *The Fastest Hound Dog In The State of Maine* was already well established long before the first windy raconteur wasted anybody's time with the shaggy dog. Whether or not there is any relationship between the two stories, as to which influenced which, I do not know. Comparison of the texts will show many

82

differences between the two tales, and this one is technically superior in every way.

Parenthetically, if anybody needs the shaggy dog story for purposes of comparison, it runs somewhat like this: An Englishman offered a large sum for "the shaggiest dog in the world." Word went around, and a man in Melbourne, Australia, had a dog which had been often called the shaggiest in the world. On the long trip to England, numerous people saw the dog, and in every instance they would say, "Why, he is without a doubt the shaggiest dog in the world." This led the owner of the dog to assume that he would be gladly welcomed, and the reward would be his. But when the Englishman saw the dog, his reaction was to say, "Hm-m-m-m, I don't think he's so shaggy." This ends the story, no matter how long it has taken to get the dog to England,

and the listener has, of course, been duped. Not so this story, which rewards the reader handsomely until he is grateful. Many people have learned what a "shaggy dog story" is without having heard the original story that created the name for a type. I explain this to gain forgiveness for having intruded it here for study purposes. Parentheses closed.

Line 224, *late mother*. I proudly call attention to the use, here, of the word "late" in an unexpected juxtaposition. I, personally, added this word to the story, and have observed that it has been accepted generally. I was at a Grange meeting once and heard two men discussing the death of a horse, which one of them referred to as, "my late mare."

It was a touching moment, and I thought to add it to the hound-dog yarn when I told it once at an Author's Luncheon at the Copley Plaza Hotel in Boston. Not only am I pleased at being able to add a touch to the story, but I point to the addition as proof that this is a folk tale, and is still a-making. I have been tempted at times to add the word "lamented" but have refrained on the grounds that restraint is, itself, an attribute of true art.

Line 236, *can't take a dog* . . . This rule prevails on all regular and well-operated railroads, and should not be construed as a peculiarity of the Bangor & Aroostook. Perhaps a moral thought could be inserted here by saying that sometimes railroads haul worse things than dogs. One time a carload of woodsmen was being taken from Bangor to a lumber camp up north, and a fight among the men made a hound sound like a wiser cargo. It seems a large and healthy group of men had been rounded up by means of getting them drunk, just as seamen were once shanghaied, and the train started off before they sobered up. Shortly one of the men referred rudely to his seat companion as "Baldy," possibly because he had no hair on his head. The hairless one took umbrage at this and gave a fair imitation of homicide all up and down the car. When the train got to Greenville all the windows had been punched out, filling the car with invigorating air, most of the passengers were unconscious, and Baldy had locked himself in the toilet until his enemies cooled off. But the railroad has always refused to let hound dogs ride in the coaches.

Line 263, *only an hour late.* The time element, in relation to the train schedule, becomes important at this point. There is an old story that a

Bangor & Aroostook train was on time one day and everybody missed it, and the conductor's casual reference to being "only" an hour late is probably in keeping with the earlier customs on this line. However, the reader will see a narrative purpose, and not a time-table meaning, in this line.

Line 279, *Mister*. The word Mister is never used in Maine except in formal introductions, or to address the moderator at town meeting and the speaker of the house of representatives. To use it on the poor conductor indicates strained relationships.

Line 294, *find somebody dumber*. Following the use of the word "Mister" (line 279), this reference is about as severe as anybody in Maine would care to go if his intentions are peaceful.

Line 310, *just as lief*. Occasional Scottish, Welsh and Saxon words are heard in Maine speech, and "just as lief" is fairly common. Sometimes you'll hear, "just as liefer."

Line 324, *worth while to the dog*. This thoughtful touch, making the dog a partner to the wager, was no doubt much appreciated.

Line 330, *runner*. A drummer, a traveling salesman.

Line 342, *seem to be*. President Bixler calls this sort of reluctant agreement, "logical positivism." It is thoroughly Maine, where men want the full facts before they negotiate an opinion. The classic example is the oldie:

"Is that a white horse?"

"Seems to be from this side."

Line 343, *forty-five minutes*. Cf. line 263 (supra).

Line 360, *Do you want to pay me now?* One time Lester Buck was beating me at a cribbage game. It was my first count and he had one hole to go. I was 37 holes behind. "Give up?" asked Buckie. "No," I said. "Deal them out." So he dealt, and when I cut he turned up a jack and won the game. But, if I had beaten him, it would have been a notable accomplishment. Generally speaking, Maine men forfeit their constitutional rights only upon dying, and to suggest that a bet be paid off prior to absolute proof of victory would certainly be construed as, "rubbing it in." We don't concede.

Line 366, *Mars Hill*. See note on line 8. Mars Hill is a farming community about mid-way of the Aroostook potato country. Its ungeographical appearance in this story is unexplained. Probably the author liked the sound, and no other explanation is needed.

Line 386, *hypering*. Going like the mill tail of Hell. This is an interesting Maine word. The prefix "hyper-" means over, above, beyond, etc., and while it has been used for centuries in combinations, it remained for down-east solecists to evolve it into a self-sufficient verb, to hyper. No matter what anybody else does, you can better them by hypering.

Line 388, *in cahoots*. This means that the conductor had privily and surreptitiously enlisted the aid of the engineer in an effort to win the bet by unfair means. To be in cahoots connotes chicanery. Does "cahoots" come from "cohorts"? Probably not. The Maine word "logan," meaning an inlet cove of a lake or pond, has always been considered a derivative of "lagoon," and such obvious deductions can fool you. Logan really comes from *lochan*, a small lake to a Scot.

Line 400, *thirty-five minutes*. Cf. lines 343 and 263 (supra).

Line 424, *mistrust*. This is a hard word to tune again once it is taken from oral Maine. It has the effect of "suspicion" when used as a verb, e.g., "I suspicioned things was confused." In this story it conveys merely that the owner of the dog thinks he has just lost 50¢.

Line 464, *feeling pretty bad*. This is the Maine equivalent of dying from grief.

Line 465, *Pay me, etc.* The power of simplicity is shown throughout this story, but here it becomes tremendous. This brief description of the happy conductor, shouting and rubbing his hands, serves to conjure up in the listener's mind a frenzy of glad joy, exuberance to the point of excess. It has, as you can see, led the artist to draw just such a picture. Yet what the artist did laboriously and at the expense of time, the story-teller has done at the cost of six simple words. There aren't above a half dozen instances in all literature where a craftsman gets so much effect from such slight effort.

Line 479, *sick conductor*. Balance this line against lines 465 and 466. "La chute en est jolie," as they say in Fort Kent.

91

Line 483, *hot box*. A bearing, or journal, fitting which has not been suitably, or recently, greased will, under the friction of momentum, become hot, making a train look as if one of the wheels is on fire. In railroad circles, the presence of a hot box is signaled to a train crew by holding the nose with the fingers, and in severe cases a train will have to stop and cool down a "hot box."